GRADE 2
GRAMMAR 2

Fun-filled Activities

Om KiDZ

An imprint of Om Books International

He-him/She-her

We use **he** and **him** to refer to a male and **she** and **her** to refer to a female.

1. Look at **Jack. He** is eating pasta.
2. Tell **him** to hurry up.
3. Today is **Jane's** birthday. **She** is 3 years old.
4. Don't buy a ticket for **her**.

Rewrite the sentences using he, she, him or her in place of the underlined nouns.

QUICK CHECK

We use **he** and **she** in naming part of a sentence. Whereas **him** and **her** are used in telling part of a sentence.

1. John asks Mary to help <u>John</u> choose a pet.
   John asks Mary to help him choose a pet

2. First John wanted a dog. Then <u>John</u> wanted a cat.
   First John wanted a dog. Then he wanted a cat.

3. John said to <u>Mary</u>, "Cats don't need baths, they don't need walks."
   John said to her "Cats don't need bath, they don't need walks."

4. <u>Mary</u> said, "Dogs like to play. They can learn tricks."
   She said, "Dogs like to play. They can learn tricks

5. <u>John</u> talked to Mom and Dad. They asked <u>John</u> to take votes.
   He talked to mom and dad. They asked him to take votes.

6. Tomorrow <u>John</u> is going to get a dog. We know exactly what kind.
   Tomorrow he is going to get a dog. We know exactly what kind.

Try it! Write five sentences about your friends using he, him, she and her.
My friend Claire likes her pet dog OREO.

They-them

Read the sentences. Choose the correct pronoun from the parentheses to complete the sentence.

1. Jason and Nora are going to the Maldives. (We, they) are at the airport.

2. Other travellers walk in the airport. Nora wonders where (she, they) are going.

3. Some of (their, them) are excited.

4. Others look tired and bored. So (they, you) talk to each other.

5. Nora and Jason are in the queue.

   (Them, they) see the queue moving.

6. Jason goes to the clerks. (He, they)

   put Jason's bags on a moving belt.

7. The clerks give Jason and Nora (him, their) luggage.

8. The people were moving to the gate. (They, she) will soon board the plane.

Possessive Pronouns

A possessive pronoun shows who or what owns something.

For example:
Where is **his** bag?
Here is **her** book.

Read the pronouns and sort them using the colour code. Write them under the correct categories.

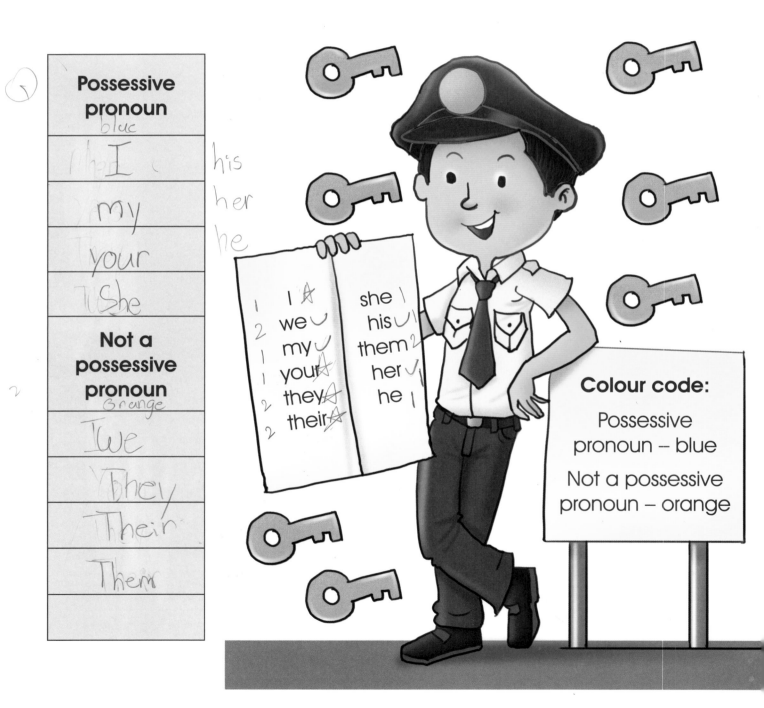

Possessive pronoun
blue
I
my
your
she

Not a possessive pronoun
orange
we
they
their
them

his
her
he

I ✗
we ✓
my ✓
your ✗
they ✗
their ✗
she
his ✓
them
her ✓
he

Colour code:
Possessive pronoun – blue
Not a possessive pronoun – orange

Possessive Pronouns-my, your-our

A possessive pronoun takes the place of a possessive noun. A possessive pronoun shows who or what owns something. **My, your, his, her, its, our, your and their** are possessive pronouns.

For example:
This is **my** globe. This is **your** map.

Tick the correct possessive pronoun in the bracket for each sentence.

1. (Me, My✓) favourite explorer is Christopher Columbus.

2. (His✓, He) three ships were called the *Niña*, *Pinta*, and *Santa Maria*.

3. (Him, His✓) most important discovery was that of America.

4. (We, Our✓) teacher told us more about Christopher's voyages.

5. In (he, his✓) calculations, Columbus thought that Asia would be 2,400 miles from Portugal.

6. I took (my✓, me) map and followed the route.

7. Poppy is tracing his journey on (her, their✓) map.

8. Sarah was the one to find the route in (she, her✓) map.

Try it! Which pronoun would you use to replace your name? Use the pronoun and its possessive form to make three sentences.

_____

Underline the possessive pronoun that completes each sentence correctly. Write it on the blank.

1. "I will show you _____(my, me, I) new friends," said Tim.

2. Kayla wanted to show off _____(she, her, its) unusual friend too.

3. Sammy climbed up and put _____(his, you, me) hand on the branch.

4. "Should we cover _____ (her, my, our) eyes?" Ina asked.

5. "Hold on to _____ (your, its, their) hats, friends!" Tim said with a grin.

6. _____(your, its, our) friends are not like other usual friends," Sally said.

7. "What's in _____ (me, their, its) pouch?" Kayla asked.

8. "_____(their, his, its) pouch is to nourish the baby" Tim said.

Possessive Pronouns

Circle the incorrect use of possessive pronouns in the sentences below. Write them correctly.

1. What is yours favourite thing to do in summer vacation?

2. Mine family visits a different theme park every summer.

3. Yang has his' own idea of building a theme park.

4. There would be only roller coasters in his's.

5. Millie said that her would have water rides and a veggie park.

6. I would have a mix of everything in mine's.

7. That ride is fun because of it's fast speed.

8. Next vacation my parents and I will visit ours favourite theme park.

QUICK CHECK

Mine, his, yours, theirs are also possessive pronouns. They refer to the nouns in subject.

Try it! Use the pronouns my and mine in sentences of your own.

Subject-verb Agreement

A verb must agree with a noun or pronoun in the subject part of a sentence. A singular subject takes a singular verb and a plural subject takes a plural verb.

Example:
He picks a flower.
They smell the rose.

Fill in the blanks with the correct form of verbs.

1. We _____ food at the new cafe. (buy, buys)

2. I _____ at the menu first. (look, looks)

3. It _____ us different things available at the cafe. (tell, tells)

4. She _____ the beverages section in the menu. (read, reads).

5. We _____ juice and shakes the most. (like, likes)

6. He _____ sandwich and juice. (choose, chooses)

7. I _____ to have fruits too. (want, wants)

8. The food _____ yummy. It is healthy too. (taste, tastes)

QUICK CHECK

We add –s or –es to the verbs when the pronoun is singular. Adding –s or –es also denote that the action is happening in the present.

Subject-verb Agreement

Write the verb that completes each sentence. Colour the matching hearts.

1. Susane and Pam _____ making cards for their parents.

2. They _____ a lot of cards to make.

3. Now Susane _____ cutting out hearts.

4. She _____ some red and white paper.

5. Pam _____ a handful of glitter to add to each one.

6. The hearts _____ red and golden.

7. The glitter _____ shiny.

8. Each card _____ a nice note on it.

9. Pam _____ an envelope for each card.

10. The cards _____ special because they are handmade.

Try it! Choose three nouns or pronouns from this page. Write each one in a sentence with a different verb.

Subject-verb Agreement

Circle the word that completes each sentence.

1. We (grow, grows) pumpkins on our farm.

2. My father (plant, plants) the seeds in spring season.

3. My mother and I (watch, watches) the little plants all summer long.

QUICK CHECK

We use **am, is, was** and **have** with the pronoun I. **Is, am** and **was** are used with singular pronoun and have with plural pronouns. Use of **have** with **I** is exceptional.

4. The bees (buzz, buzzes) around the pumpkin blossoms.

5. In a few days, the first pumpkin (begin, begins) to grow.

6. We (help, helps) dad to pick the pumpkins.

7. I (choose, chooses) one pumpkin and carry it into the house.

8. Mom cuts it into pieces and (scoop, scoops).

9. Then she (bake, bakes) a pumpkin pie.

10. All of us (love, loves) pumpkin pie.

Pronoun-verb Agreement

Read the paragraph and find the mistakes. Then rewrite the paragraph correctly.

Dad and I goes to the library. He read how to grow carrots. I reads *A Kid's Guide to Gardening*. The book tell us how to grow a garden. We wants to plant carrots, beans and potatoes. We knows it takes hard work. For a while, it seem that nothing happens. We waits patiently, and soon green shoots appear. One day I sees some white blossoms. I like gardening.

_____

_____

_____

_____

_____

_____

Contractions

A contraction is a short form of two words put together. An apostrophe (')
takes the place of the letter or letters that are left out. Some contractions
are formed by putting together pronouns and verbs.

Example:

I am   I'm   she is   she's   he is   he's

Circle the words in bold. Write the contractions.

1. **We will** take care of the earth.   _____

2. **We are** planting many trees.   _____

3. **It is** good to pick up litter.   _____

4. **He will** turn off the lights.   _____

5. **Let us** take a bike instead of a car.   _____

6. **Who will recycle** cardboard boxes today?   _____

7. **They have** been recycling newspapers.   _____

8. **You are** a friend of the earth!   _____

Word bank

you're	we'll
they've	It's
we're	let's
He'll	who's

Contractions

Circle the contraction that completes each sentence. Then write it on the blank.

1. _____ forget the car keys.   Don't   Dont'
2. I think _____ beautiful.   Its   it's
3. The flowers _____ wrapped.   aren't   arent'
4. _____ the red blossom.   There's   theres
5. We _____ have any orchids.   didn't   did'nt
6. She _____ want tulips.   doesnt   doesn't
7. They _____ been watered.   haven't   havent'
8. This _____ my vase.   Isn't   isn't
9. _____ working today?   Who's   whos
10. _____ a great flower shop.   That's   that's

QUICK CHECK

Remember that an apostrophe takes the place of the letter or letters that are left out of a contraction. Apostrophe is always used with the second word. Like- have not will be written as haven't and not hav'nt.

Contractions

Possessive pronouns, such as **their**, **your**, and **its** do not have apostrophes.

Possessive Pronoun
its
their
your

Contraction
you're
it's
they're

Read each sentence. Write the correct pronoun or contraction on the line.

1. (They're, Their)_____ teacher is teaching a lesson about the moon.

2. (Their, They're) _____ reading the book Rocket to the Moon.

3. (Its, It's) _____ about the first landing on the moon.

4. Are they almost finished with _____ (they're their) book?

5. (Your, You're)_____ reading a book called The Moon.

6. What is (your, you're) _____ book about?

7. The book is about the moon and (it's, its) _____ phases.

8. (Its, It's)_____ full of interesting facts.

Contractions

Read the paragraph. Circle any incorrectly written contractions.

Im Rosa. I want to become a zoologist. Thats someone who studies animals. Until then I will learn about animals by watching and reading.

There are plenty of rabbits in our backyard. Theyve built their warren near the fence. Ive seen rabbits hop across the yard. Then suddenly theyre gone down the hole into the warren. I cant go down there! So I read about what its like inside. Then I drew a picture of it.

_____

_____

_____

_____

_____

_____

_____

_____

Try it! Rewrite the paragraph by placing each contraction with the apostrophe in the right place. Use possessive pronouns and contractions correctly.

Adjectives

Adjectives are words that describe people, places, animals and things.

Example:

The eucalyptus tree is **tall**.

I see a **blue** balloon flying high.

Choose the best adjectives for each ad below and complete it.

Lost Dog

Call Miss Sara
333-0033

Please help me find my _____ (tiny, cute) dog. It is _____ (brown, black) with a _____ (dark, light) patch on his tummy. His fur is _____ (hairy, smooth) and his tail is _____ (fuzzy, long). My dog is very _____ (nice, friendly). I miss my dog!

Lost Dog

Call Mr. Ron
666-1231

Please help me find my _____ (huge, little) dog. It is _____ (pretty, white) with _____ (black, brown) spots on it. It has _____ (long, short) ears. Its legs are _____ (slender, small). It has a _____ (white, striped) collar around its neck. I miss my dog!

Adjectives – What Kind

Some adjectives tell what kind.

For example:

pink balloons   **big** balloons

Fill in the blanks with adjectives. Use the word bank.

1. Sail around the _____ island and past the _____ ship.

2. Land on the _____ side of Secret Island.

3. Walk onto the sandy beach and around the _____ cactus.

4. Wade across the _____ pond.

5. Then hike to the _____ cave.

6. Look for the _____ rock that looks like a ball.

7. Take _____, _____ steps toward the _____ tree.

8. Dig a _____ hole until you hit something _____ like metal.

Word Bank

round
hard
west
small
sunken
deep
prickly
shallow
tallest
dark
triangular

Try it! Write directions from your classroom to the nearest water fountain.
Underline each adjective you use.

Adjectives-How Many

We use some adjectives to tell how many.
Example:
I saw **three** squirrels on the tree.
Please give me **a few** envelopes.

Circle the adjectives that tell how many. Then rewrite each sentence using another adjective.

1. Sally's birthday is in three weeks.

    _____

2. She is inviting ten friends to her birthday party.

    _____

3. Her brother Sam is blowing up a few balloons.

    _____

4. There will be nine candles on her cake.

    _____

5. One candle is for good luck.

    _____

6. There will be many sweet
    treats in the party.

    _____

Try it! Look around and write down names of ten things you see. Use adjectives to describe them.

Comparison of Adjectives

We can use adjectives to compare people, places or things. Add -er to an adjective to compare two nouns.

Example:

This pencil is longer than that pencil.

| Big | Bigger | Biggest |
| Long | Longer | Longest |

Add –er to the adjectives and complete the table.

Adjective	Add – er	Adjective	Add – er
Small		Tall	
Warm		Cool	
Bright		Thick	
Hard		Long	
Soft		Thin	
Smart		Slow	
Quiet		Dark	

Comparison of Adjectives

Fill in the blanks with the correct form of the adjectives.

1. Hammy's Hat Store is a _____ (new, newer) store in the city.

2. The prices at his store are _____ (low, lower) than prices in the town.

3. The fur hats are _____ (warm, warmer) than the other hats.

4. They are _____ (soft, softer) than the straw hats.

5. The straw hats are _____ (cheap, cheaper) and nice.

6. They are also _____ (small, smaller) than the cowboy hats.

7. The cowboy hats have a _____ (high, higher) price.

8. _____ (wide, wider) hats in the store have flowers on them.

9. It is _____ (nice, nicer) than the straw hats.

10. Hammy keeps her store _____ (clean, cleaner) and tidy.

QUICK CHECK

Adjectives that end in –er are usually used with than. We also don't use articles a or an with them.

Comparison of Adjectives

Write the adjectives that complete each sentence.
Then circle the adjective in the puzzle.

1. The children are dressed for
   the _____ costume party.
   (grander, grandest)

2. The fairy is _____ than the
   clown. (taller, tallest)

3. The clown's laugh is _____ than
   the cowboy's laugh. (louder, loudest)

4. The fairy has the _____
   costume at the party. (fancier,
   fanciest)

5. The pirate is _____ than the
   fairy. (plump, plumper)

6. The fairy wants the _____
   apple in the basket. (smaller,
   smallest)

7. The cowboy's bag of candy is
   _____ than the pirate's.
   (bigger, biggest)

8. These are the _____ party
   guests. (happier, happiest)

```
A  Z  Y  P  L  U  M  P  E  R
T  K  C  N  B  I  G  G  E  R
S  V  R  E  D  U  O  L  S  K
E  S  M  A  L  L  E  S  T  D
D  O  F  A  N  C  I  E  S  T
N  T  I  J  T  D  F  B  L  Q
A  T  S  E  I  P  P  A  H  K
R  N  D  H  V  D  A  S  P  H
G  P  P  V  O  E  L  K  O  Y
R  E  L  L  A  T  V  F  B  N
```

Try it! Write a few sentences on a fancy costume party. Use adjectives to compare the people at the party.

Adjectives That Compare

Add –er or –est to the base word and write the adjective on the blank.

1. Bella thinks tennis is the _____ sport of all. (great)

2. Her new racquet is _____ than her old one. (light)

3. She can swing the new racquet _____ than the old one. (fast)

4. Now her serves are _____ than her brother's. (quick)

5. She is still the _____
   player on the team. (young)

6. But she is also the _____
   of them all! (fast)

7. The other team's player is
   _____ than Bella. (tall)

8. But she has practiced _____
   than he has! (hard)

9. Bella wants to be the _____
   player in her school. (great)

10. She hopes to win the _____
    trophy she has ever won. (big)

Try it! Write three sentences using adjectives on this page. Write them in the –est form.

Adverbs

An **adverb is a word that** tells more about a verb.
An adverb can tell how, when and where.

Example:
The bird flew **swiftly**.
The word **swiftly** tells how the bird flew.

QUICK CHECK

Adverbs that tell how usually end in –ly. We can form such adverbs by adding –ly to adjectives.
Loud + ly = loudly
Soft + ly = softly

Circle the verb in each sentence. Then write the adverb on the line.

1. Julia spoke enthusiastically about her robot to the class.

   _____

2. Everyone listened carefully to her.

   _____

3. Henry pulled the lever gently.

   _____

4. The robot moved suddenly and walked around.

   _____

5. The students cheered loudly for the robot.

   _____

6. The clever robot bowed gracefully.

   _____

Try it! Think of any 5 adjectives. Add –ly to each and change it to an adverb.

Adverbs

Underline the verb in each sentence. Then circle the adverb and write it on the chart below.

1. Rosh walks toward a sleeping lion.
2. He firmly holds his camera.
3. Lee hides behind Rosh.
4. Yesterday, Lee scared a dog.
5. Today, Lee remembers to be quiet.
6. The lion quietly moves one eye.
7. Now Rex takes a picture.
8. The lion roars loudly.
9. Lee and Rosh stand still.
10. Lee and Rosh sneak away.

How?	When?	Where?

Using Adverbs

Write a sentence about each picture. Use the adverb.

1. playfully _____

_____

2. carefully _____

_____

3. quickly _____

_____

4. neatly _____

_____

5. lovingly _____

_____

6. slowly _____

_____

Adverbs That Tell How

Read the sentences about Nancy's garden. In each sentence, circle the adverb that tells how. Then write the adverb in the matching space.

1. Nancy absolutely loves gardening.
2. She mostly grows carrots and lettuce.
3. When spring arrives, Nancy carefully plans her garden.
4. She plants very tiny seeds.
5. Then she quickly waters the soil.
6. Every day, Nancy works to keep other insects from greedily eating her plants.
7. Months later, she lovingly admires her garden.
8. Then Nancy gently picks her vegetables and shares them with her friends.

1.
2.
3.
4.
5.
6.
7.
8.

What type of insect is aphid? To find out match the circled letter in each word to a line below.

___ ___ ___ ___ ___ ___ ___ ___
 7   3   6   4   1   5   8   2

Adverbs That Tell When

We also use adverbs to tell when.

Example:

I painted a picture yesterday.

Read each sentence. Choose the adverb that tells when.

1. Linda wakes up _____. (early, peacefully)

2. She takes her morning walk_____ (slowly, first)

3. _____ she eats breakfast and hurries back outside. (quickly, then)

4. _____ she gets her gardening tools. (happily, next)

5. She's ready to start working _____. (hard, now)

6. Linda will _____ leave a weed in her garden. (not, never)

7. She works _____ every day. (busily, late)

8. She waters the plants _____. (last, deeply)

Using adverbs

Write a sentence using each adverb.

1. Outside _____

_____

2. Today _____

_____

3. Everywhere _____

_____

4. Never _____

_____

5. Long ago _____

_____

6. Finally _____

_____

7. Often _____

_____

Look at the picture and write a paragraph on it. Use three nouns, three adjectives and three adverbs in the paragraph.

_____

_____

_____

_____

_____

_____

Answer Key

Page 2

1. Him
2. He
3. Her
4. She
5. He, him
6. He

Page 3

1. they
2. they
3. them
4. they
5. they
6. they
7. their
8. they

Page 4

Possessive pronoun
My, your, their, his, her
Not a possessive pronoun
I, we, they, she, them, he

Page 5

1. my
2. his
3. his
4. our
5. his
6. my
7. her
8. her

Page 6

1. my
2. her
3. his
4. our
5. your
6. Your
7. its
8. their

Page 7

The pronouns in bold are incorrect.

1. What is **yours** favourite thing to do in summer vacation?
   Correct form - your.

2. **Mine** family visits a different theme park every summer.
   Correct form- My.

3. Yang has **his'** own idea building a theme park. Correct form - his.

4. There would be only roller coasters in **his's**. Correct form - his.

5. Millie said that **her** would have water rides and a veggie park.
   Correct form - her.

6. I would have a mix of everything in **mine's**. Correct form - mine.

7. That ride is fun because of **it's** fast speed. Correct form - its.

8. Next vacation my parents and I will visit **ours** favourite theme park.
   Correct form - our.

Page 8

1. buy
2. look
3. tells
4. reads
5. like
6. chooses
7. want
8. tastes

Page 9

1. are
2. have
3. is
4. has
5. has
6. are
7. is
8. has
9. has
10. are

Page 10

1. grow
2. plants
3. watch
4. buzz
5. begins
6. help
7. choose
8. scoops
9. bakes
10. love

Page 11

Dad and I **go** to the library. He **reads** how to grow carrots. I read A Kid's Guide to Gardening. The **book** tells us how to grow a garden. We **want** to plant carrots, beans and potatoes. We **know** it takes hard work. For a while, it seems that nothing happens. We **wait** patiently, and soon green shoots appear. One day I **see** some white blossoms. I like gardening.

Page 12

1. We'll
2. We're
3. It's
4. He'll
5. Let's
6. Who'll
7. They've
8. You're

Answer Key

Page 13

1. don't
2. it's
3. aren't
4. there's
5. didn't
6. doesn't
7. haven't
8. isn't
9. who's
10. that's

Page 14

1. their
2. they're
3. it's
4. their
5. you're
6. your
7. its
8. it's

Page 15

I'm Rosa. I want to become a zoologist. **That's** someone who studies animals. Until then I will learn about animals by watching and reading. There are plenty of rabbits in our backyard. **They've** built their warren near the fence. **I've** seen rabbits hop across the yard. Then suddenly **they're** gone down the hole into the warren. I **can't** go down there! So I read about what **it's** like inside. Then I drew a picture of it.

Page 16

1st para
cute, brown, light, smooth, long, friendly
2nd para:
little, white, black, short, slender, striped

Page 17

1. small, sunken
2. west
3. prickly
4. shallow
5. dark
6. round
7. five, small, tallest
8. deep, hard

Page 18

1. three
2. ten
3. a few
4. nine
5. one
6. many

Page 19

smaller
warmer
brighter
harder
softer
smarter
quieter
taller
cooler
thicker
longer
thinner
slower
darker

Page 20

1. new
2. lower
3. warmer
4. softer
5. cheaper
6. smaller
7. high
8. wider
9. nicer
10. cleaner

Page 21

1. grandest
2. taller
3. louder
4. fanciest
5. plumper
6. smallest
7. bigger
8. happiest

Page 22

1. greatest
2. lighter
3. faster
4. quicker
5. youngest
6. fastest
7. taller
8. harder
9. greatest
10. biggest

Page 23

1. Verb- spoke, adverb- enthusiastically
2. Verb- listened, adverb- carefully
3. Verb- pulled, adverb- gently
4. Verb- moved, adverb- suddenly
5. Verb- cheered, adverb- loudly
6. Verb- bowed, adverb- gracefully

Page 24

1. verb: walks, adverb: toward
2. verb: holds, adverb: firmly
3. verb: hides, adverb: behind
4. verb: scared, adverb: yesterday
5. verb: remembers, adverb: today
6. verb: moves, adverb: quietly
7. verb: takes, adverb: now
8. verb: roars, adverb: loudly
9. verb: stand, adverb: still
10. verb: sneak, adverb: away

How?	When?	Where?
Firmly	Yesterday	Away
Quietly	Today	Toward
Loudly	Now	behind
Still		

Answer Key

Page 25

Children will do on their own.

Page 26

1. absolutely
2. mostly
3. carefully
4. very
5. quickly
6. greedily
7. lovingly
8. gently

Page 27

1. early
2. first
3. then
4. now
5. hard
6. not
7. busily
8. last

Page 28

Children will do on their own.

Page 29

Children will do on their own,